Mr. Educator
Making Learning Fun!

Introducing Algebra 2:
Specialising and
Generalising

Mr. Educator
Making Learning Fun!

Algebra Series

Introducing Algebra 1: Number Patterns and Sequences
Introducing Algebra 2: Specialising and Generalising
Introducing Algebra 3: Introducing Equations
Introducing Algebra 4: Equations and Graphs

Aussie Tales: Developing Morals and Values in KS2 and 3

Teaching Guide
Blubber and Floss
Jimmy and the Bluebottles
Macca Dacca
Magpie Madness
No Presents for Christmas
Ratbags
Shape Shifters
The Copperhead
The Crossover
The Football

Aber Education Teacher Books

Survival Teen Island: The Ultimate survival guid for teenagers
Family relationships
Bullying and Conflict
Hey Thompson
Self-Esteem and Values
Self-Esteem: a manual for mentors
Enhancing Self -Esteem in the adolescent
Grief, illness and other issues

Self-Help

Write yourself well
Choose Happiness
The Eat well stay slim budget cookbook

More titles in development

Introducing Algebra 2: Specialising and Generalising

Dr Graham Lawler MA. PhD, Adv. Dip Educ., Cert Ed CATL.

Mr. Educator
Making Learning Fun!

The range of Mr Educator Books has been developed in response to needs expressed by tutors, students and governmental agencies. The materials are appropriate for students who require support in advancing their numeracy and literacy skills.

Dr Graham Lawler is an author and editor with over 29 years of experience in teaching from primary level to university post-graduate level, curriculum material development and publishing.

Introducing Algebra 2: Specialising and Generalising

ISBN 978-1-84285-080-0

Aber Education

Aber House
P.O. Box 225
Abergele
Conwy County LL18 9AY

Published by Aber Publishing

www.aber-publishing.co.uk

<u>Developing Mathematical Thinking</u>
<u>Teacher Notes</u>

There is a fundamental skill in algebra, which is also an essential life skill, and that is the ability to generalise from a given situation.

Colleagues are asked to consider real-life experiences where such generalising is a normal part of everyday life. For example: If I need to put up shelves and each shelf takes 4 screws, how many screws do I need?

The number of screws $= 4 \times$ the number of shelves.

Here we have created a word equation, which is a rule. This rule applies regardless of the number of shelves we need to put up and therefore it is a general rule. This is what we mean by generalising in mathematics.

The purpose in this booklet is to develop the student's thinking ability in generalising situations. To achieve this we are looking at situations where we are looking for what is the same. The students need to be encouraged to look for the 'sameness' in the situation. They then need to be encouraged to write down the rule that explains that 'sameness'.

The second stage in developing this level of mathematical thinking is to develop a 'rule' that explains all cases in the situation being described. We then want to encourage pupils/students to record their results and then to move to subsequent shorthanding of that rule. So for example the rule:
The number of screws is four times the number of shelves

Moves to
Screws $= 4 \times$ shelves

To
$S = 4H$ (where S represents the number of screws and H represents the number
           of shelves)

And then hopefully...

to $x = 4y$

This will occur when the pupil recognises that it is the relationship that is significant rather than the symbol and that S $= 4H$ and $x = 4y$ are essentially the same rule.

Lesson Aims and Objectives
   All books in the Mr Educator list (from GLMP Ltd) are written with aims as intentions and objectives as outcomes written in terms of the child's behaviour. This then affects the assessment of learning and therefore such precision is to be welcomed.

How to start an investigation in mathematics

There are 3 pieces of advice to remember when introducing children to investigations:

- Keep them short
- Keep them simple
- Keep them obvious

'Doing Mathematics'

The process of doing mathematics involves many components

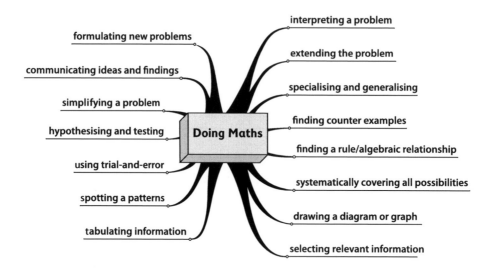

This is an indication of some of the thinking skills we want the children to develop, but very often they become like a plumber with a toolkit full of tools but they are unsure of which tool to use. Therefore it becomes necessary to create a recurring structure to the work:

- Doing some mathematics
- Organising the results
- Spotting Patterns, finding the rule

Your Use of Language

Colleagues are advised to try and always be as positive as possible with children. Remember we are trying to get the child thinking, so we need to mentally stand back and ask questions like:

'What do you think?'

'Why?'

If possible, try to avoid being negative, even when the child is wrong, by using phrases like:

'I see you have started off well but you seem to have got lost on the way'.

This then does not affect the child's self-esteem, and keeps them learning. Many adults have difficulty with negative feedback, so for some adults, and particularly politicians to suggest this is political correctness are actually displaying their own shallow level of thinking.

All teachers are advised to avoid what has been dubbed ' teacher lust' which is defined as the overwhelming desire to explain.

Personal, Learning and Thinking Skills

The PLTS provide a framework for describing the skills and qualities that the children and students in your school need for success in learning and life. PLTS form advanced thinking skills, which refer to cognitive skills that involve a higher-level thinking that is more than just memory and recall. Advanced level thinking requires the learner to use knowledge in some purposeful way.

The framework is built around three curriculum questions:

- What are we trying to achieve?
- How will the learning experience of the children be organised?
- What evidence will we use to determine that our aims have been achieved?

The PLTS framework is online at
http://curriculum.qcda.gov.uk/uploads/PLTS_framework_tcm8-1811.pdf

and therefore we do not wish to replicate it here. However we do want to draw your attention to the different groups of thinkers. In terms of curriculum development, it is essential that teacher colleagues understand that the implementation of thinking skills in this manner needs to be integrated into the curriculum and not simply bolted on. Bolt on curriculum initiatives make the curriculum unwieldy and do not lead to long-term curriculum improvements.

The PLTS framework identifies six groups of skills:

- Independent enquirers
- Creative thinkers
- Reflective learners
- Team workers
- Self-Managers
- Effective participators

Children will usually encounter skills from several groups in any one learning experience.

In planning lessons we suggest the following framework could be helpful.

Teacher:			Supported by:				Period:		Date:	
Subject:	Topic: Intro to algebra: looking for what is the same	Year:		Set:			No in group:			
PLTS*	Independent Enquirers	Creative Thinkers	Team Worker	Self Manager	Effective Participator		Reflective Learner			

Context:	This lesson would be suited to being the first lesson of the topic, where students are being introduced to algebra. This lesson can be adapted to suit pupils of all abilities and ages.
Concepts:	Competence – applying life knowledge to analyse for similarity. Creativity – students combine reasoning to define commonality.
Processes:	Representing – they represent their views of commonality Analysing – they explore different circumstances and see commonality in real life. Interpreting – They interpret the commonality and use the worded descriptions. Communication – they engage in mathematical discussion to describe commonality
Range and Content:	Mathematics – Introduction to algebra Team Workers and Creative Thinkers
Curriculum Opportunities:	Students develop confidence in analysing situations and developing generalised thinking.
Lesson Overview	In this lesson students examine different situations and find 'the sameness' in real life
Lesson Aim	The lesson is aimed at pupils working at Level 5 and above, although can be adapted to lower ability pupils
Learning Outcomes/ Objectives:	To introduce students to the ' commonality' of a characteristic in a set. At the end of this lesson the students should be able to: • describe the common characteristics of a set verbally and /or in writing • talk to/listen to and evaluate their own and the views of others. It is vital as part of the learning process that the students are aware of the purpose of the lesson. To this end we use the WALT acronym (see below).
Resources	• Aber Education Worksheets • Whiteboard
Assessment Strategies	• Peer Assessment • Teacher Informal assessment
Opps for ICT/ Language/ Numeracy	• Numeracy – discouraging the use of a calculator for straightforward calculations
Links to wider curriculum including PSHE/ Citizenship	• Team Working building skills • Listening Skills

* (personal learning & thinking skills) PLTS underpin the whole curriculum and can transform young people's engagement with learning. They support learners' understanding

Starter

Look at the class and look for something that is the same about the students. Are the students all wearing school uniform?
The purpose of this warm up activity is to get them thinking of the 'sameness' in each situation.

Introduce them to WALT.
On the board write down

W_e A_{re} L_{earning} T_o

Then write down

Look for the rule that tells us what is the same about a group of things.

It is important that students have a sign-posted idea of where they are going and it is also important that parents see this in their student's work.

Suggested groups of students to make up

1 all boys/girls

2 all students wearing a white shirt

3 all students wearing brown shoes/black shoes

4 all students wearing a blue/black jumper

The purpose here is simply to get the students to look for the 'sameness' in real situations.

Main Activity

- Ensure the students have a copy of each of these photographs and encourage them in groups to write positive statements about the commonality of each photograph
- Make sure all students have a chance to engage with the photos

Consolidation

The students are to work through the worksheets.

Plenary

Talk through the fact that there is commonality in all of the photographs and that this 'sameness' is the important characteristic that you are discussing.

Name _____**Teacher's Name** _____

W_e A_{re} L_{earning} T_o   Look for the 'samness' in things.

<u>What is the same?</u>

Look at these photographs, what can you see in the photograph that is the same?

1

2

3

4

5

6

7

8

9

10

W_e A_{re} L_{earning} T_o

Look for the rule that tells us what is the same about a group of things.

Starter

Remind the students of the last lesson where they looked for the 'sameness'

Main activity

Make up an example on the board, for instance

2	4	6	8	10
4	8	12	16	20

Now ask questions like, ' what do I need to do to 2 that gets me to 4?'

'What do I need to do to 4 to get me to 8?' and so on.

This is developing the student's ability to generalise and you need to encourage them to develop a sense that the same operation is happening to the top line and that 'sameness' is what you are after.

Consolidation

Students work through the worksheets that follow.

Plenary

Ask students to supply answers for each of the questions, ensure the whole class agrees.

Name _____**Teacher's Name** _____

Start/End Game

W_e A_{re} L_{earning} T_o find the rule

In each of the following cases, complete the table and find the rule that links the start numbers and the end numbers, the first one is done for you. In some examples you will have to complete

Start	2	4	6	8
End	4	8	12	16

Rule: End number = 2 × start number

Here is a top tip. Look at all of the start numbers; you have to do the same thing to each of them, to get the end numbers, that is your rule.

1

Start	1	2	3	4	5	6
End	2	3	4	5	6	7

Rule:

2

Start	2	3	4	5	6	7
End	6		12	15		21

Here you need to fill in the missing gaps and then find the rule.

Rule:

3

Start	5	10	15	20	25
End	10	15		25	

Here you need to fill in the missing gaps and then find the rule.

Rule:

4

Start	3	6	9	12	15	18	21
End	9	18	27	36	45	54	63

Rule:

On this page make up six start/ends of your own. Then swap with another person and see if they can work out the rule.

Top Tip: Make sure that you check the numbers in your start/ends and that they are all correct.

On the board write down

W_e A_{re} L_{earning} T_o work with number machines

Starter

Talk about the function of a machine. Stress that the machine operates on the input to make an output. Show the images of the machines and stress how they take an input operate or 'work on it' and then get an output.

Main activity

Draw a number machine on the board and go through the process of operating on the numbers

Consolidation

Students work through the worksheets that follow.

Plenary

Ask students to supply answers for each of the questions, ensure the whole class agrees.

<u>Machines</u>

Traian Vuia's flying machine

Thermal cycler for PCR

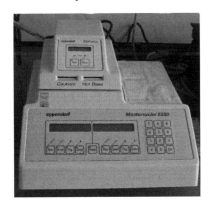

Early Mower

Name _____**Teacher's Name** _____

Number Machines

We **A**re **L**earning **T**o use number machines and find inputs and outputs

Here is a diagram for a number mapping. It shows what happens to a number as it goes through a number machine.

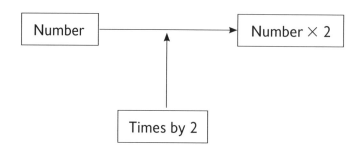

Look at what this means. It tells us that whatever number you put into the machine, it multiplies it by 2 to get the output. So say you put 3 into the machine, it would multiply this by 2 to get 6.

Complete the following by filling in the spaces

1

Times 2

4 ⟶ ___

12 ⟶ ___

16 ⟶ ___

2

Substract 4

6 ⟶ ___

24 ⟶ ___

10 ⟶ ___

Remember, convince yourself then convince another person.

Mr. Educator
Making Learning Fun!

Now fill in the gap for the first number. What number will give you the answer?

3

Times 2

___ ——→ 22

___ ——→ 14

___ ——→ 30

4

Subtract 4

___ ——→ 4

___ ——→ 12

___ ——→ 15

5

Add 6

13 ——→ ___

4 ——→ ___

___ ——→ 28

6

Divided by 2

6 ——→ ___

18 ——→ ___

___ ——→ 30

7

× by 3

2 ——→ ___

___ ——→ 15

17 ——→ ___

8

Divided by 7

___ ——→ 3

56 ——→ ___

77 ——→ ___

The next group of number machines are slightly harder. They use two-step number mappings, from a two step number machine.

Here is an example

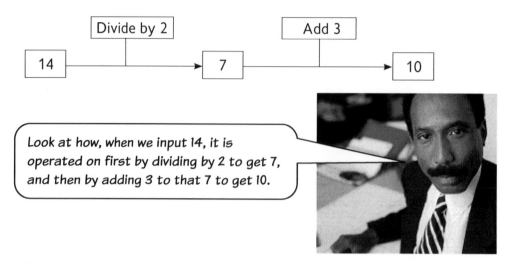

Look at how, when we input 14, it is operated on first by dividing by 2 to get 7, and then by adding 3 to that 7 to get 10.

Now try these

1

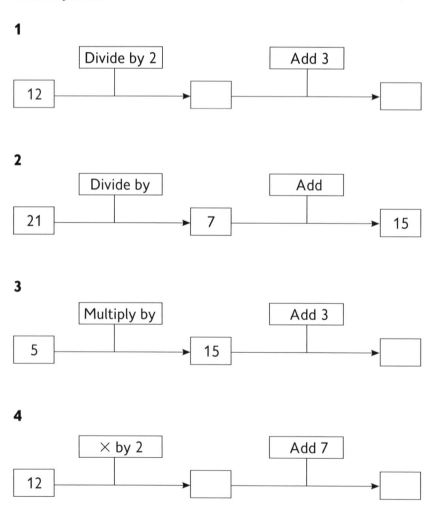

2

3

4

Mr. Educator
Making Learning Fun!

5

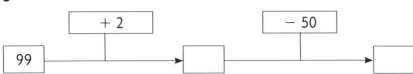

6

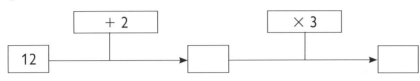

7

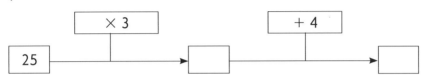

8

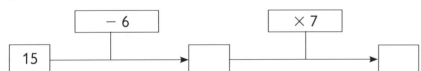

Top Tip: convince yourself then convince another person.

Mr. Educator
Making Learning Fun!

Chains

WALT: investigate and look at numbers and patterns

Look at this chain:

6 ———————➤ 3 ———————➤ 10 ———————➤ 5 ———————➤ 16 ———————➤ ......

Rules:

- If a number is even divide it by 2
- If a number is odd multiply by 3 and add 1

- Continue the chain that is written above.
- What happens?

- Try 7 as your starting number, then try 8, then try other numbers
- What happens?

Now try changing the rules:
e.g. change the second rule

- If a number is odd, multiply it by 3 and then subtract 1
- Try using 6 as a starting number now
- What happens?
- Is it the same as before?
- Try other starting numbers.

Palindromes

WALT: investigate and look at numbers and patterns

- Choose any number   216
  Reverse the digits   + 612
  And add   828

- What do you notice about 828 (Hint: look at 828 backwards)

You can see that 828 is a palindrome (reads the same backwards as well as forwards)

- Try another number   154
  Reverse and add   + 451
            605

- 605 is not a Palindromic number (a palindrome) so the process has to be repeated

$$
\begin{array}{r}
605 \\
+\ 506 \\
\hline
1111
\end{array}
$$

- 1111 is a palindrome

Does this always happen?

Investigate

Possible Extensions

- are palindromic numbers multiples of 11?
- Can you always make a palindromic number by adding a number and its reverse?

Subtraction Patterns

WALT: investigate and look at numbers and patterns

5		11		8		15		
	6		3		7		10	
		3		4		3		4
			1		1		1		1
				0		0		0

- This is a subtraction pattern which starts with the numbers 5, 11, 8, 15

- How do we get the other numbers?

- Try starting a new pattern with 19, 7, 4, 26

- Can you make a subtraction pattern starting with 2 digit numbers, which is less than 5 lines long?

- Investigate for different sets of starting numbers

Handshakes: a whole class investigation

- We are now moving the children from number based work towards generalising. On the next two pages there are three whole class teacher led investigations to develop the skill in tackling an investigation in mathematics, they are:

- **Try some out**
- Draw diagram and then tabulate results
- Look for patterns and then look for the rule

This first activity is also designed to show the children the need to model problems to a more manageable level. Ask the whole class to stand up and link hands with everyone.

- How many handshakes will take place for the whole class? For this investigation when two people shake hands, that is counted as one handshake.

This is probably far too big for the children to cope with and so there is a teaching opportunity here, but we need to simplify the problem. We need to model the problem and make it simpler. Make sure you explain to the children that modelling (i.e. making the problem smaller and easier to understand) is a common strategy used by mathematicians.

- Choose five children to come out to the front of the class.

- Ask the children to form a circle and then shake hands with all of the other people.

- How many handshakes took place?

Suggest to the children that a diagram may be a useful way to see who has shaken hands with whom.

Bhavna

John

Nisha

Philip

Judith

Bhavna

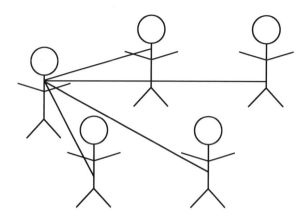

Now ask the class to draw a diagram to show all of Bhavna's handshakes

We only have a limited amount of space here so if you set up a table of results for the number of children and the number of handshakes, you should find the number of hand-shakes is in fact the series of triangle numbers, although if the children have not yet seen this series there is no need to mention it yet. See Number Patterns and Sequences – the first in this series for – more on triangle numbers.

Number of children	Numbers of handshakes
1	0
2	1
3	3
4	6
5	10
6	15

Ask the class if they can spot a pattern in the table. What do they think it will be for 7 children and how can they tell?

So the recurrent themes here are :

- **Try some out**

- **Draw diagram and then tabulate results**

- **Look for patterns and then look for the rule**

Moving Squares

This is a people game where you have 9 carpet tiles and 8 children.

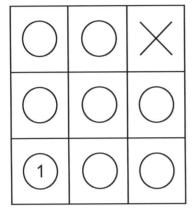

Here the objective is to get the child we have marked 1 to the empty square we have marked X.
The rules are that it is only possible to move backwards or forwards and side-to-side (i.e. NOT diagonally).

Some teachers place a large floppy hat on child 1 to make him/her obvious to all; we will leave this to your judgement.

As before the children may find this too big to deal with so model it - i.e. make it smaller. Try a 2 × 2 square, then come back to a 3 × 3, and so on.

Remember the recurrent themes

- **Try some out**
- **Draw diagram and then tabulate results**
- **Look for patterns and then look for the rule**

Frogs

This is an old favourite and great fun in the classroom. The objective is to get the girls to where the boys are and the boys to where the girls are. In single sex schools this may need to be people wearing ties to non-ties or something similar.

| 3 girls | empty | 3 boys |

Set up a table of results for 3 × 3 then 4 × 4 and so on.

In terms of PLTS you are developing their thinking skills since these activities force the children to think ahead and visualise the outcomes. This activity is great fun, and there is not enough fun in mathematics classrooms!

Part 2   Teacher Notes

In the following work we will reinforce the recurrent theme mentioned above
The theme is:

1   Try some out. This means to actively either to draw some patterns or, using building blocks, to build some models. And the students need to be encouraged to do at least six of these examples.

2   Then build a table of results. The teaching points here need to explain that there are two variables in most cases they are clear and shaded tiles. The students need to count the numbers of each variable (clear tiles or shaded tiles, wheels or cars) and record them in the table.

3   Then, using the skills covered in the start/end activity earlier in this booklet, they need to find the rule that connects the two variables.

4   Encourage the students to look for 'what is the same' about the table of results. 'What mathematical operation do I do to one set of numbers to get the second set of numbers' ,and emphasise that the operation is always the same thing.

5   Always encourage students to look at the differences in the right hand side of the table. If they are the same - eg going up by 3 each time - then this tells the student to multiply by 3 and then make any adjustments

eg

x	y		
1	5	$8 - 5 = 3$	so multiply x by 3 i.e. $3x + ? = y$
2	8	$11 - 8 = 3$	the ? must be 2 so the equation is
3	11	$14 - 11 = 3$	$3x + 2 = y$
4	14		

Obviously it takes time to get to this stage so students will be given easier relationships to establish at first.

In the following situation of Bridges we are trying to develop the students to think through the situation and get to something like:

The number of clear tiles = the number of shaded tiles + 4 or something similar.

Students who can move quiclz might summarise to something like

$C = S + 4$ or similar

Bridges

Bridge 1

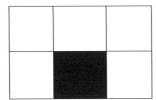

Clear Tiles	Shaded Tiles

a) 1 shaded tile, how many clear tiles? _____

Bridge 2

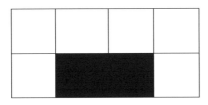

b) 2 shaded tiles, how many clear tiles? _____

c) Now draw bridges for

3 shaded, how many clear tiles?
4 shaded, how many clear tiles?
5 shaded, how many clear tiles?
6 shaded, how many clear tiles?
7 shaded, how many clear tiles?
8 shaded, how many clear tiles?

Fill in the table as you go, putting in the number of clear tiles in the left column and the number of shaded tiles in the right column.

d) What is the rule that connects the number of clear tiles and the number of shaded tiles. Write your rule here.

Top Tip: Check your rule by convincing yourself, then convincing another person. If they are not convinced, is your rule correct?

Sandwiches

Shaded Tile	Clear Tiles

a) 1 shaded tile, how many clear tiles?_____

b) 2 shaded tiles, how many clear tiles?_____

c) Draw out a sandwich with 3 shaded tiles and write down the number of clear tiles._____

d) Draw at least six different sized sandwich shapes and complete the table.

e) What is the rule that connects the number of clear tiles and the number of shaded tiles.

Write your rule here. _____

Check your rule with a different number of clear and shaded tiles, say 10 shaded tiles. Predict what the number of clear tiles should be then check your prediction.

Double Sandwiches

Double sandwiches always start and end with two clear tiles.

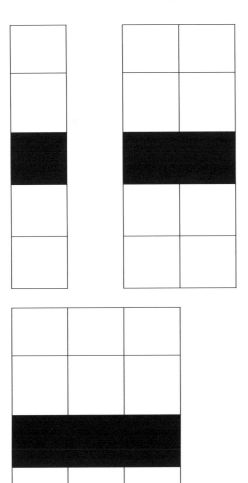

Shaded Tile	Clear Tiles

a) 1 shaded tile, how many clear tiles?_____

b) 2 shaded tiles, how many clear tiles?_____

c) Draw out a sandwich with 4 shaded tiles and write down the number of clear tiles._____

d) Draw at least six different sized sandwich shapes and complete the table.

e) What is the rule that connects the number of clear tiles and the number of shaded tiles.

Write your rule here. _____

Single Towers

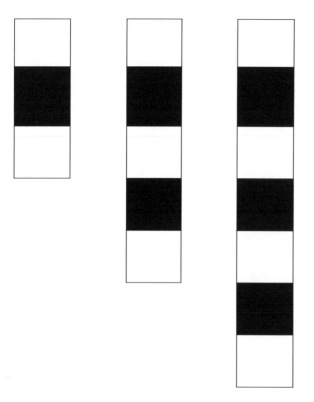

Shaded Tile	Clear Tiles

These are single towers. Single towers ALWAYS start and end with a single clear tile.

a) Two clear tiles, how many shaded tiles?_____

b) Three clear tiles, how many shaded tiles? _____

c) Four clear tiles, how many shaded tiles? _____

d) Draw at least six different sized single towers and complete the table.

e) What is the rule that connects the number of clear tiles and the number of shaded tiles? Write your rule here. _____

Check your rule with a different number of clear and shaded tiles. Predict what the number of clear tiles should be then check your prediction.

Mr. Educator
Making Learning Fun!

Double Towers always start and end with two clear tiles

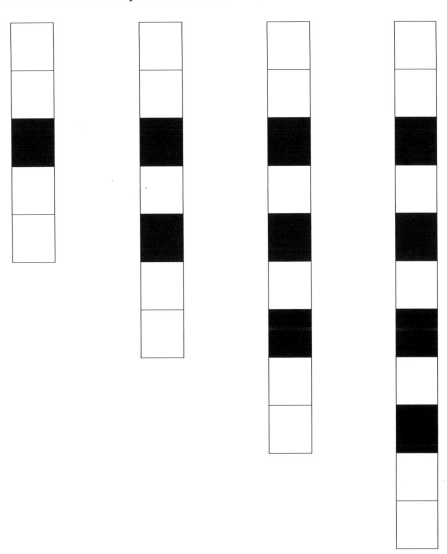

a) Four clear tiles, how many shaded tiles?_____

b) Five clear tiles, how many shaded tiles? _____

c) Six clear tiles, how many shaded tiles? _____

d) Draw at least six different sized single towers and complete a table.

e) What is the rule that connects the number of clear tiles and the number of shaded tiles? Write your rule here. _____

Making Learning Fun!

Cars

Remember the format, try out at least six different numbers of cars, build a table and then find the rule, then check your rule.

For the purposes of this investigation we are treating all cars as having 4 wheels.

a) 1 car, how many wheels?_____

b) 3 cars, how many wheels? _____

c) Build up a table of results for cars and wheels.

d) Look at the results in your table, what is the rule that connects the number of cars with the number of wheels?

e) Write your rule here_____

f) Test your rule by applying a different number of cars into your rule? Does it work? Convince yourself, then convince another person.

What would the rule be if you were investigating six wheeled lorries?

34

<u>Shelves</u>

I put up the shelves for my book collection. Each shelf took 4 screws to attach it firmly to the wall. Investigate for the number of shelves and the number of screws.

Don't forget to write a rule for the number of shelves and the number of screws. In this investigation shelves and screws start with an S so use a different letter for one of them. Usually in maths we use *a* or *x*.

Mr. Educator
Making Learning Fun!

Fences Investigation

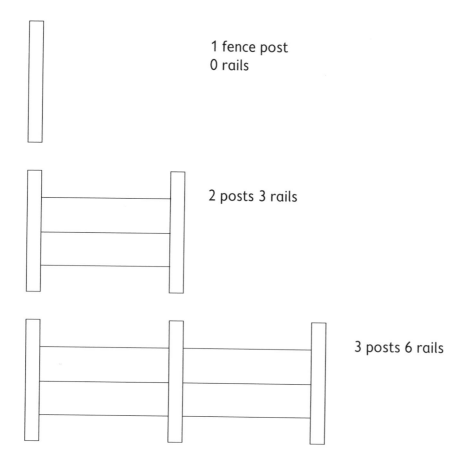

1 fence post
0 rails

2 posts 3 rails

3 posts 6 rails

- Draw the diagram for 4 posts, 5 posts, 6 posts
- Make up a table like this

Posts	Rails
1 ⟶	0
2 ⟶	⟶
3 ⟶	⟶
4 ⟶	⟶
5 ⟶	⟶
6 ⟶	⟶

Can you predict how many railings 7 posts would have?

What about 8 posts, 9 posts, 10 posts?

Draw the diagrams to prove you are right.

Can you find a rule that connects the number of posts and the number of railings?

Bricks investigation

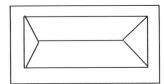 1 brick, 0 joins

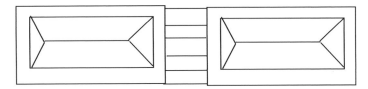 2 bricks
1 join

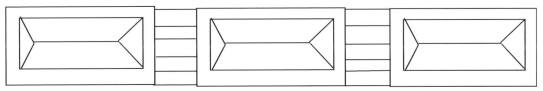

3 bricks
2 joins

- Draw diagrams for 4 bricks, 5 bricks and 6 bricks
- Make up a table of results like this

Can you predict what will happen for 10 posts?

Bricks	Joins
1	
2	
3	
4	
5	
6	

- What about 50 posts?

- How could you test your predictions?

- Write down the rule that connects the number of bricks and the number of joins.

Stick Maths

You can do amazing things with sticks.

Look at these awesome cars, all made from matchsticks.

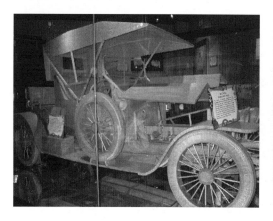

This is a model of Hogwarts from the Harry Potter books and it is all made from matchsticks, about 60 000 matchsticks. But please don't mess about with matches; my friend did and he got badly burned and ended up in hospital!

Mr. Educator
Making Learning Fun!

Sticks 1

We are moving onto stick maths now. Think about it in the same way as other investigations; and remember what I said before. Try out at least six different versions, build a table of results, find the rule.

Draw pattern 4 and 5 in this sequence. Make a table for the first six patterns in this sequence. Build up a table of pattern number and sticks, so pattern 1 is 6 sticks Look at the differences in the table, use this to find the rule

Pattern	Sticks
1	6
2	
3	
4	
5	
6	

Sticks 2

Draw pattern 5 and 6 in this sequence. Make a table for the first six patterns in this sequence. Look at the differences in the table; use this to find the rule.

Pattern	Sticks
1	4
2	
3	
4	
5	
6	

Remember, in an investigation like this, convince yourself then convince another person.

Mr. Educator
Making Learning Fun!

Sticks 3

Draw patterns 4, 5 and 6 in this sequence. Make a table for the first six patterns in this sequence.
Look at the differences in the table; use this to find the rule.

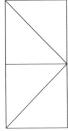

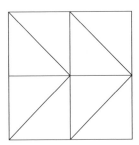

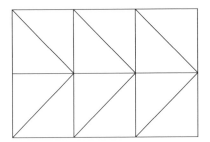

Pattern	Sticks
1	4
2	
3	
4	
5	
6	

Mr. Educator
Making Learning Fun!

Sticks 4

Draw patterns 4, 5 and 6 in this sequence. Make a table for the first six patterns in this sequence. Look at the differences in the table; use this to find the rule.

Pattern	Sticks
1	3
2	
3	
4	
5	
6	

When I have convinced myself, I try and convince my dad that my answer is right. If he is not convinced I go back and look again to check if I have made a mistake.

I wish mathematics had been this much fun when I was your age!

Mr. Educator
Making Learning Fun!

Sticks 5

Draw patterns 4, 5 and 6 in this sequence. Make a table for the first six patterns in this sequence.
Look at the differences in the table; use this to find the rule.

Pattern	Sticks
1	4
2	
3	
4	
5	
6	

Sticks 6

Draw patterns 4, 5 and 6 in this sequence. Make a table for the first six patterns in this sequence. Look at the differences in the table; use this to find the rule.

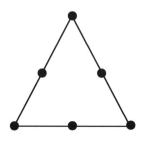

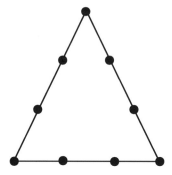

Pattern	Sticks
1	3
2	
3	
4	
5	
6	

Check your rule by putting in some numbers and see that it works. If the figures do not work, check your rule. Then when you have convinced yourself that your rule is right, convince another person.

Mr. Educator
Making Learning Fun!

Sticks 7

Draw patterns 4, 5 and 6 in this sequence. Make a table for the first six patterns in this sequence.
Look at the differences in the table; use this to find the rule.

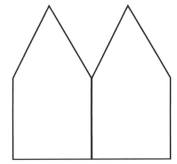

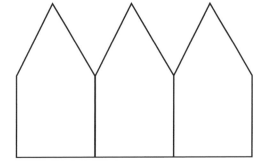

Pattern	Sticks
1	5
2	
3	
4	
5	
6	

Mr. Educator
Making Learning Fun!

Sticks 8

Draw patterns 4, 5 and 6 in this sequence. Make a table for the first six patterns in this sequence.
Look at the differences in the table; use this to find the rule.

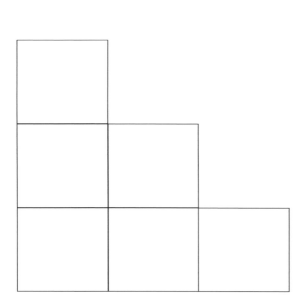

Pattern	Sticks
1	4
2	
3	
4	
5	
6	

Making Learning Fun!

<u>Fishponds</u>

I am planning to build a pond. The grey tiles show the water the clear tiles show flagstones around the pond.

Draw patterns 4, 5 and 6 in this sequence. Make a table for the first six patterns in this sequence.
Look at the differences in the table; use this to find the rule.

Pattern	Flagstones
1	8
2	
3	
4	
5	
6	

47

Squares

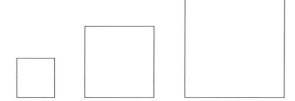

> Here you need to draw at least the next three shapes and set up a table of pattern number against sticks. So pattern 1 is the smallest shape and has 4 sticks.
> Pattern 2 has 8 sticks and so on.
> Fill in the table and look for a rule.

> Don't forget; convince yourself, then convince another person.

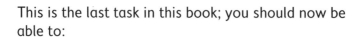

This is the last task in this book; you should now be able to:

- Try some out

- Draw diagrams and then tabulate results

- Look for patterns and then look for the rule

Word Search

P	Y	M	G	K	E	A	D	A	P
A	M	J	P	T	C	B	W	L	T
T	D	M	O	R	J	A	J	G	L
T	O	H	C	I	R	C	L	E	H
E	T	U	O	A	O	U	D	B	K
R	Q	I	R	N	U	R	U	R	L
N	Z	F	H	G	N	F	Q	A	W
B	H	S	I	L	D	S	B	I	L
T	A	B	L	E	B	S	B	A	E
N	E	Q	U	A	T	I	O	N	A

Cross Number

1		**2**			**3**		■	**4**	**5**		**6**	
	■		■		**7**					■		
8						■	**9**					
	■		■		**10**	**11**				■		
	■	■		**12**	**13**			■	**14**		■	
■		**15**		■		■					■	**19**
16				**17**	**18**							
		■		■		■				■		
■		**20**	**21**			■			**22**		■	
23						**24**						
	■	**25**			■				■			
26					■	**27**						

Across
1 one hundred and ninety nine thousand five hundred and twenty two in numbers
2 9500 + 22
3 1 + 1
4 6998+103
5 98 + 3
7 1100 + 250
8 one hundred thousand in figures
9 two thousand and one in figures
10 five thousand four hundred in figures
11 2 x 200
12 55 x 10
13 25 x 2
16 200 - 2
17 seventy five thousand in figures
18 5 x 1000
20 244 x 2
21 8 x 11
23 18 500 + 255
24 thirty five thousand in figures
25 44 x 20
26 2600 - 16
27 one hundred and ninety thousand in figures

Down
1 eleven thousand and ninety nine + one hundred and one
2 nine thousand + one hundred and one
3 twenty one thousand + fifty five in figures
4 7600 - 80
5 one million and nine hundred in figures
6 990 + 20
7 one thousand and fifty + five in figures
8 50 x 2
10 5 x 11
11 5 x 8
12 five million five hundred and seventy thousand eight hundred and fifty in figures
14 450 x 2
15 two millions eight hundred and thirty four thousand seven hundred and eighty eight in figures
16 9 x 2
19 99 999 + 1
20 4800 - 12
21 8500 + 84
22 1999+1
23 (11 x 11) + 1
25 4 x 22

50

Answers

P10 -12

1 people		**2** trucks		**3** racing cars		**4** lipsticks
5 women		**6** miners		**7** planets
8 people on beach		**9** dogs		**10** cats

p14

1 start $+ 1 =$ end   **2** 9, 18, start $\times 3 =$ end   **3** 20, 30 start $+ 5 =$ end
4 start $\times 3 =$ end

p18-19

1 8, 14, 32	**2** 2, 20, 6	**3** 11, 7, 15
4 7, 15, 18	**5** 19, 10, 22	**6** 3, 9, 15
7 6, 5, 51	**8** 21, 8, 11	

p20

1 6,9	**2** 3, 8	**3** 3, 18	**4** 60, 67	**5** 101, 51
6 14, 42	**7** 75, 79	**8** 11, 77		

p22 Chains 8,4,2,1,4,2,1

p29 Bridges **a)** 5 **b)** 6 **c)** 7,8,9,10,11,12 **d)** $c = s + 4$

p30 Sandwiches **a)** 2 **b)** 4 **c)** 6 **e)** $c = 2s$ photo answer$= 20$ clear

p31 Double sandwiches **a)** 4 **b)** 8 **c)** 16 **e)** $c = 4s$

p32 Single Towers **a)** 1 **b)** 2 **c)** 3 **e)** $c = s + 1$ or $s = c - 1$

p33 **a)** 1 **b)** 2 **c)** 3 **e)** $c - 3 = s$ (or $s + 3 = c$)

p34 **a)** 4 **b)** 12 **e)** $c = 4w$

p36 Table results are $3, 6, 9, 12, 15$ and the rule is $3p - 3 = r$

p 37 Table results are 0, 1, 2, 3, 4 and the rule is $j = b - 1$

p39 Table results are 6, 11, 16, 21, 26, 31 and the rule is $5p + 1 = s$

p40 Table results are 7, 10, 13 and the rule is $s = 3p + 1$

p41 Table results are 9, 16, 23, 30, 37, 44 and the rule is $7p + 2 = s$

p42 Table results 3, 5, 7, 9, 11, 13 and the rule is $2p + 1 = s$

p43 Table results 4, 8, 12, 16, 20, 24 and the rule is $s = 4p$

p44 Table results 3, 6, 9, 12, 15, 18 and the rule is $s = 3p$

p45 Table results are 5, 9, 13, 17, 21, 25 and the rule is $4p + 1 = s$

p46 Table results are 4, 10, 16, 22, 28, 24 and the rule is $6p - 2 = s$

p47 Table results are 8, 10, 12, 14, 16, 18 and the rule is $f = 2p + 6$

P								A	
A				T				L	
T				R				G	
T			C	I	R	C	L	E	
E				A	O			B	
R				N	U			R	
N				G	N			A	
				L	D				
T	A	B	L	E					
	E	Q	U	A	T	I	O	N	

[1]1	9	[2]9	5	2	[3]2	■	[4]7	[5]1	0	[6]1
2	■	1	■	■	[7]1	3	5	0	■	0
[8]1	0	0	0	0	0	■	[9]2	0	0	1
0	■	1	■	■	[10]5	[11]4	0	0	■	0
0	■	■	■	[12]5	[13]5	0	■	[14]9	■	■
■	[15]2	■	■	5	■	■	■	0	■	■
[16]1	9	8	■	[17]7	[18]5	0	0	0	■	[19]1
8	■	3	■	0	■	■	■	■	■	0
■	[20]4	[21]8	8	■	■	■	■	[22]2	■	0
[23]1	8	7	5	5	■	[24]3	5	0	0	0
2	■	[25]8	8	0	■	■	■	0	■	0
[26]2	5	8	4	■	[27]1	9	0	0	0	0